The approved documents

What is an approved document?

The Secretary of State has approved a series of documents that give practical guidance about how to meet the requirements of the Building Regulations 2010 for England. Approved documents give guidance on each of the technical parts of the regulations and on regulation 7 (see the back of this document).

Approved documents set out what, in ordinary circumstances, may be accepted as reasonable provision for compliance with the relevant requirements of the Building Regulations to which they refer. If you follow the guidance in an approved document, there will be a presumption of compliance with the requirements covered by the guidance. However, compliance is not guaranteed; for example, 'normal' guidance may not apply if the particular case is unusual in some way.

Note that there may be other ways to comply with the requirements – *there is no obligation to adopt any particular solution contained in an approved document.* If you prefer to meet a relevant requirement in some other way than described in an approved document, you should discuss this with the relevant building control body.

In addition to guidance, some approved documents include provisions that must be followed exactly, as required by regulations or where methods of test or calculation have been prescribed by the Secretary of State.

Each approved document relates only to the particular requirements of the Building Regulations that the document addresses. However, building work must also comply with any other applicable requirements of the Building Regulations.

How to use this approved document

This document uses the following conventions.

a.   Text against a green background is an extract from the Building Regulations 2010 or the Building (Approved Inspectors etc.) Regulations 2010 (both as amended). These extracts set out the legal requirements of the regulations.

b.   Key terms, printed in green, are defined in Appendix A.

c.   When this approved document refers to a named standard or other document, the relevant version is listed in Appendix C (documents) or Appendix C (standards). However, if the issuing body has revised or updated the listed version of the standard or document, you may use the new version as guidance if it continues to address the relevant requirements of the Building Regulations.

NOTE: Standards and technical approvals may also address aspects of performance or matters that are not covered by the Building Regulations, or they may recommend higher standards than required by the Building Regulations.

Where you can get further help

If you do not understand the technical guidance or other information in this approved document or the additional detailed technical references to which it directs you, you can seek further help through a number of routes, some of which are listed below.

a. The Government website: www.gov.uk

b. *If you are the person undertaking the building work:* either from your local authority building control service or from an approved inspector

c. *If you are registered with a competent person scheme:* from the scheme operator

d. *If your query is highly technical:* from a specialist or an industry technical body for the relevant subject.

The Building Regulations

The following is a high level summary of the Building Regulations relevant to most types of building work. Where there is any doubt you should consult the full text of the regulations, available at www.legislation.gov.uk.

Building work

Regulation 3 of the Building Regulations defines 'building work'. Building work includes:

a. the erection or extension of a building

b. the provision or extension of a controlled service or fitting

c. the material alteration of a building or a controlled service or fitting.

Regulation 4 states that building work should be carried out in such a way that, when work is complete:

a. *For new buildings or work on a building that complied with the applicable requirements of the Building Regulations:* the building complies with the applicable requirements of the Building Regulations.

b. *For work on an existing building that did not comply with the applicable requirements of the Building Regulations:*

   (i) the work itself must comply with the applicable requirements of the Building Regulations

   (ii) the building must be no more unsatisfactory in relation to the requirements than before the work was carried out.

Material change of use

Regulation 5 defines a 'material change of use' in which a building or part of a building that was previously used for one purpose will be used for another.

The Building Regulations set out requirements that must be met before a building can be used for a new purpose. To meet the requirements, the building may need to be upgraded in some way. The requirements of Part Q apply to a material change of use, but where only part of a building is subject to building work, only that part of the building need meet the requirements of Part Q.

Materials and workmanship

In accordance with regulation 7, building work must be carried out in a workmanlike manner using adequate and proper materials. Guidance on materials and workmanship is given in Approved Document 7.

Energy efficiency requirements

Part 6 of the Building Regulations imposes additional specific requirements for energy efficiency.

If a building is extended or renovated, the energy efficiency of the existing building or part of it may need to be upgraded.

Notification of work

Most building work and material changes of use must be notified to a building control body unless one of the following applies.

a. It is work that will be self-certified by a registered competent person or certified by a registered third party.

b. It is work exempted from the need to notify by regulation 12(6A) of, or Schedule 4 to, the Building Regulations.

Responsibility for compliance

People who are responsible for building work (e.g. agent, designer, builder or installer) must ensure that the work complies with all applicable requirements of the Building Regulations. The building owner may also be responsible for ensuring that work complies with the Building Regulations. If building work does not comply with the Building Regulations, the building owner may be served with an enforcement notice.

Contents

Approved Document Q: Security

Summary

0.1 This approved document gives guidance on how to comply with requirement Q1 of the Building Regulations. It contains the following sections:

Section 1: Doors
Section 2: Windows
Appendix A: Key terms
Appendix B: Bespoke timber secure doorsets
Appendix C: Documents referred to
Appendix D: Standards referred to

Application

0.2 The guidance in this approved document applies to new dwellings only; this includes dwellings formed by a material change of use.

Requirement Q1: Unauthorised access

This approved document deals with the following requirement from Part Q of Schedule 1 to the Building Regulations 2010.

Requirement

Requirement	Limits on application
PART Q SECURITY **Unauthorised access**	
Q1 Reasonable provision must be made to resist unauthorised access to— (a) any dwelling; and (b) any part of a building from which access can be gained to a flat within the building.	Requirement Q1 applies only in relation to new dwellings.

Performance

Requirement Q1 applies to easily accessible doors and windows that provide access in any of the following circumstances:

a. into a dwelling from outside

b. into parts of a building containing flats from outside

c. into a flat from the common parts of the building.

In the Secretary of State's view, doors and windows will meet requirement Q1 if they can resist physical attack by a casual or opportunist burglar by being both:

a. sufficiently robust

b. fitted with appropriate hardware.

Section 1: Doors

General

1.1 All easily accessible doorsets (including garage doorsets and communal entrance doorsets) that provide access into a dwelling or into a building containing a dwelling should be secure doorsets in accordance with paragraphs 1.2 to 1.4.

NOTE: If a garage has no interconnecting doorset allowing access into the dwelling, garage doorsets need not be secure doorsets. Where access to the dwelling can be gained via an interconnecting doorset from the garage, then either the garage doorset (pedestrian and vehicular) or the interconnecting doorset should be a secure doorset.

Design of secure doorsets

1.2 Secure doorsets should be either:

a. manufactured to a design that has been shown by test to meet the security requirements of British Standards publication PAS 24:2012, or

b. designed and manufactured in accordance with Appendix B.

NOTE: Doorsets satisfying other standards that provide similar or better performance are also acceptable. These standards include:

- STS 201 Issue 5:2013

- LPS 1175 Issue 7:2010 security rating 2

- STS 202 Issue 3:2011 burglary rating 2

- LPS 2081 Issue 1:2015 security rating B.

Further advice is available in Secured by Design's *New Homes 2014*.

1.3 Letter plates, where provided, should:

a. have a maximum aperture of 260mm x 40mm, and

b. be located and/or designed to hinder anyone attempting to remove keys with sticks and/or insert their hand, for example by incorporating a flap or other features to restrict access.

NOTE: Letter plates meeting the requirements of the Door and Hardware Federation's (DHF) technical specification TS 008:2012 have been shown to protect against the attacks mentioned above.

1.4 The main doors for entering a dwelling (usually the front door) should have a door viewer unless other means exist to see callers, such as clear glass within the door or a window next to the doorset. The same doorset should also have a door chain or door limiter.

NOTE: In some situations a door chain or limiter is not appropriate, for example where a warden may need emergency access to residents in sheltered housing. Alternative caller-identification measures, such as electronic audio-visual door entry systems, can be used to identify visitors.

Installation and fixing of secure doorsets

1.5 Frames should be mechanically fixed to the structure of the building in accordance with the manufacturer's installation instructions.

1.6 Lightweight framed walls should incorporate a resilient layer to reduce the risk of anyone breaking through the wall and accessing the locking system.

The resilient layer should be timber sheathing at least 9mm thick, expanded metal or a similar resilient material. The resilient layer should be to the full height of the door and 600mm either side of the doorset.

Section 2: Windows

General

2.1 Ground floor, basement and other easily accessible windows (including easily accessible rooflights) should be secure windows in accordance with paragraphs 2.2 and 2.3.

Design of secure windows

2.2 Windows should be made to a design that has been shown by test to meet the security requirements of British Standards publication PAS 24:2012.

NOTE: Windows satisfying other standards that provide similar or better performance are also acceptable. These standards include:

- STS 204 Issue 3:2012

- LPS 1175 Issue 7:2010 security rating 1

- LPS 2081 Issue 1:2015 security rating A.

Further advice is available in Secured by Design's *New Homes 2014*.

Installation and fixing of secure windows

2.3 Frames should be mechanically fixed to the structure of the building in accordance with the manufacturer's installation instructions.

Appendix A: Key terms

Doorset
A complete door assembly, assembled on site or delivered as a completed assembly, consisting of the door frame, door leaf or leaves, essential hardware and any integral side panel or fanlight (but excluding coupled assemblies).

Window
Windows, rooflights, roof windows and similar.

Secure doorset
Either:
- a doorset that is proven to resist physical attack by a casual or opportunist burglar, or
- a bespoke doorset incorporating construction features that are proven to reduce crime.

Secure window
Either:
- a window that is proven to resist criminal attack, or
- a bespoke window incorporating construction features that are proven to reduce crime.

Easily accessible
Either:
- a window or doorway, any part of which is within 2m vertically of an accessible level surface such as the ground or basement level, or an access balcony, or
- a window within 2m vertically of a flat or sloping roof (with a pitch of less than 30°) that is within 3.5m of ground level.

Coupled assembly
A doorset and window that are supplied as separate self-contained frames and fixed together on site.

Proven
(In the context of secure doorsets and secure windows) – a product designed and constructed in accordance with a specification or design shown by test to be capable of meeting the required performance.

Further information on materials and workmanship is given in Approved Document 7.

NOTE 1: Laboratories accredited by the United Kingdom Accreditation Service (UKAS) or an equivalent European national accreditation body should have the necessary expertise to conduct the relevant tests.

NOTE 2: Any test evidence used to confirm the security of a construction should be carefully checked to ensure that it demonstrates compliance that is adequate and that applies to the intended use. Evidence passed from one organisation to another can become unreliable if important details are lost. Small differences in construction can significantly affect the performance of a doorset or window.

NOTE 3: Schemes that certify compliance with PAS 24:2012 or other standards that offer similar or better performance may be acceptable for demonstrating compliance. A list of UKAS-accredited certification bodies is given on the UKAS website. Many recognised schemes are also listed in Secured by Design's *New Homes 2014*, Section 2.

Appendix B: Bespoke timber secure doorsets

B.1 A timber doorset constructed in accordance with this appendix is considered a secure doorset for the purposes of requirement Q1.

> **NOTE:** The information in this appendix applies to doors of up to 1000mm wide and 2000mm high. Additional measures may be necessary for larger doorsets

Material

B.2 The doorset should be manufactured from solid or laminated timber with a minimum density of 600kg/m^3.

Dimensions

B.3 Door rails, stiles and muntins should be at least 44mm thick. After rebating, frame components should retain at least 32mm of timber.

B.4 Any panel within the doorset should be at least 15mm thick. The panel should be securely held in place. Beading should be mechanically fixed and glued in position.

B.5 The smaller dimension of each panel – which can be either the width or height of the panel – should be 230mm or less.

Locks, hinges and letter plates

B.6 The main doors for entering a dwelling (usually the front doorset) should be fitted with a multipoint locking system that meets the requirements of:

- PAS 3621 (key locking on both sides), or
- PAS 8621 (non-key locking on the internal face), or
- PAS 10621 (non-key locking on the internal face, but with an external locking override facility).

If it is not practical or desirable to install a multipoint locking system, a mortice lock that conforms with one of the following standards can be fitted instead, with a surface-mounted rim lock that conforms to the same standard:

- BS 3621 (key locking both sides), or
- BS 8621 (non-key locking on the internal face), or
- BS 10621 (non-key locking on the internal face, but with an external locking override facility).

Between the locking points for the mortice lock and surface-mounted rim lock, the distance should be 400–600mm.

B.7 The non-primary doors for entering a dwelling (for example, back door or garage interconnecting doors) should be fitted with a multipoint locking system that meets the requirements of:

- PAS 3621 (key locking on both sides), or
- PAS 8621 (non-key locking on the internal face), or

- PAS 10621 (non-key locking on the internal face, but with an external locking override facility).

If it is not practical or desirable to install a multipoint locking system, a mortice lock that conforms with one of the following standards can be fitted instead, with two morticed bolts.

- BS 3621 (key locking both sides), or
- BS 8621 (non-key locking on the internal face), or
- BS 10621 (non-key locking on the internal door face, but with an external locking override facility).

The morticed bolts should have a minimum projection of 20mm, should be at least 100mm from the top and bottom corners of the door, and should avoid any door construction joints.

B.8 Hinges accessible from outside should incorporate hinge bolts.

B.9 Letter plates, where provided, should:

a. have a maximum aperture of 260mm x 40mm, and

b. incorporate a flap or other features designed to hinder anyone attempting to remove keys with sticks and/or insert their hand.

NOTE: Letter plates meeting the requirements of the Door and Hardware Federation's (DHF's) technical specification TS 008:2012 have been shown to protect against the attacks mentioned above.

Door limitation and caller identification

B.10 The main doors for entering a dwelling (usually the front door) should have a door viewer unless other means exist to see callers, such as clear glass within the door or a window next to the doorset. The same doorset should also have a door chain or door limiter.

NOTE: In some situations a door chain or limiter is not appropriate, for example where a warden may need emergency access to residents in sheltered housing. Alternative caller-identification measures such as electronic audio-visual door entry systems can be used to identify visitors.

Glazing

B.11 Any glazing which, if broken, would permit someone to insert their hand and release the locking device on the inside of the door should be a minimum of class P1A in accordance with BS EN 356:2000. Double- or triple-glazed units need to incorporate only one pane of class-P1A glass.

Appendix C: Documents referred to

cured by Design, *New Homes 2014.* ACPO, 2014.

Appendix D: Standards referred to

British Standards

BS EN 356

Glass in building. Security glazing. Testing and classification of resistance against manual attack [2000]

BS 3621

Thief resistant lock assembly. Key egress [2007+A2:2012]

BS 8621

Thief resistant lock assembly. Keyless egress [2007+A2:2012]

BS 10621

Thief resistant dual-mode lock assembly [2007+A2:2012]

Publicly available specifications

PAS 24

Enhanced security performance requirements for doorsets and windows in the UK. External doorsets and windows intended to offer a level of security suitable for dwellings and other buildings exposed to comparable risk [2012]

PAS 3621

Multipoint locking assemblies. Keyed egress. Performance requirements and test methods [2011]

PAS 8621

Multipoint locking assemblies. Keyless egress. Performance requirements and test methods [2011]

PAS 10621

Multipoint locking assemblies. Dual mode egress. Performance requirements and test methods [2011]

Loss Prevention Certification Board

LPS 2081: Issue 1

Requirements and testing procedures for the LPCB approval and listing of building components, strongpoints, security enclosures and free-standing barriers offering resistance to intruders attempting to use stealth to gain entry [2015]

LPS 1175: Issue 7

Requirements and testing procedures for the LPCB approval and listing of intruder resistant building components, strongpoints, security enclosures and free-standing barriers [2010]

Certisecure: Warrington Certification Limited

STS 201: Issue 5

Enhanced security requirements for doorsets to satisfy the requirements of PAS 24 [2013]

STS 202: Issue 3

Requirements for burglary resistance of construction products including hinged, pivoted, folding or sliding doorsets, windows, curtain walling, security grilles, garage doors and shutters [2011]

STS 204: Issue 3

Enhanced security performance for windows to satisfy the requirements of PAS 24 [2012]

Door and Hardware Federation

TS 008

Enhanced security and general requirements for letter plate assemblies and slide through boxes [2012].